Yazoo 2
Activity Book

Unit	Page	Unit	Page
Alphabet Aa–Zz	2	**7a** There's a town.	48
Numbers 1–20	4	**7b** Where's Chatter?	50
Colours	5	**7c** Skills: My town	52
1a It's a school!	6	**8a** She can sing.	54
1b Spell 'octopus'.	8	**8b** Can you skip?	56
1c Skills: My classroom	10	**8c** Story: Where's my mobile phone?	58
2a Cars and dolls	12	Science	60
2b That's a robot!	14	Review 4	61
2c Story: The frogs!	16	**9a** We like breakfast.	62
Social Science	18	**9b** Patty likes fish.	64
Review 1	19	**9c** Skills: What's on the menu?	66
3a She's pretty.	20	**10a** He gets up at seven o'clock.	68
3b Is he your grandpa?	22	**10b** Does Rob go to the zoo every day?	70
3c Skills: My family	24	**10c** Story: Superboy!	72
4a We're cowboys.	26	Social Science	74
4b Are we pirates?	28	Review 5	75
4c Story: The grey duck	30	**11a** I'm playing a game.	76
Maths	32	**11b** They're having a shower.	78
Review 2	33	**11c** Skills: Me and my friends	80
5a It's his kite.	34	**12a** They aren't swimming.	82
5b They're our toys.	36	**12b** Are they sleeping?	84
5c Skills: Our favourite toys	38	**12c** Story: Jane and the giant	86
6a She's got a pet.	40	Social Science	88
6b Has it got wings?	42	Review 6	89
6c Story: Sam, the circus boy!	44	My Picture Dictionary	90
Science	46	Cut outs	99
Review 3	47		

Alphabet Aa – Zz

1 Look and write.

1 <u>a</u>pple

2 __ear

3 __at

4 __og

5 __lephant

6 __lower

2 Match and write.

1

2

3

<u>g</u>oat

__ippo

__nsect

__elly

__angaroo

__ion

4

5

6

Find and circle. Then write.

monkeynestoctopuspenguinqueenrabbit

1 ͬab＿＿t   **2** ＿＿st   **3** ＿on＿＿y

4 ＿u＿＿n   **5** ＿ct＿＿us   **6** ＿e＿＿ui＿

4 **Order the letters and write.**

1 ansek   **2** girte   **3** lluemabr   **4** lniovi

snake _____   _____   _____   _____

5 hlwae   **6** oxf   **7** oo-yy   **8** rbaze

_____   _____   _____   _____

Numbers 1-20

1 Look and write.

1 one	___ two	3 _____	___ four	5 _____
6 _____	___ seven	8 _____	___ nine	10 _____

2 Find and circle. Then write.

t	e	l	e	v	e	n	m
o	f	i	f	t	e	e	n
v	i	t	w	e	l	v	e
n	i	n	e	t	e	e	n
x	t	w	e	n	t	y	r
f	o	u	r	t	e	e	n
t	h	i	r	t	e	e	n

11
eleven

19
_____

13
_____

15
_____

12
_____

14
_____

20
_____

3 Write in the correct order.

10 11 12 13 _____ _____ 16 _____ _____ 19 _____

4

Colours

 Listen and colour. •))

1   6   9   3   8   10

2   11   5   7   4

② **Look at 1. Colour by number.**

5

1a It's a school!

1 Look and circle.

What's this?

1 It's a (bag) / pencil case.
2 It's a rubber / pen.
3 It's a desk / bag.

4 It's a pencil case / pencil.
5 It's a notebook / pencil case.
6 It's a bag / rubber.

2 Find and circle.

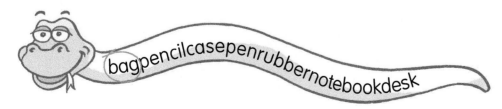

bagpencilcasepenrubbernotebookdesk

6

3 Read and match.

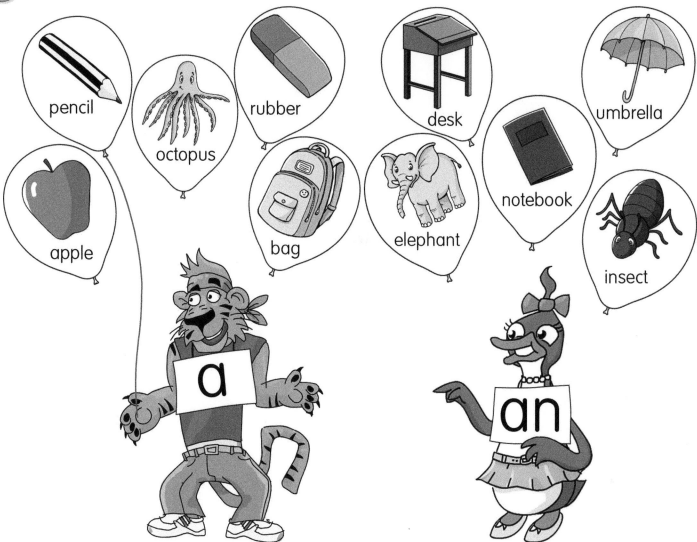

4 Look and write.

1 What's this?
It's _____ a pencil _____.

2 What's this?
It's _____.

3 What's this?
It's _____.

4 What's this?
It's _____.

5 What's this?
It's _____.

6 What's this?
It's _____.

Spell 'octopus'.

1 **Look and match.**

bag

notebook

board

pencil

ruler

pen

rubber

desk

chair

2 **What's missing in 1? Draw and write.**

1 _____

2 _____

3 _____

3 **Look and match.**

1 Be quiet, please.

2 Clean the board, please.

3 Spell 'dog', please.

4 Write 'cat', please.

Listen and colour.

5 **Read and circle. Then colour.**

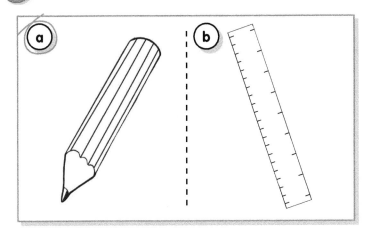

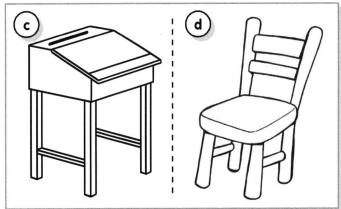

1 What's this?
It's a pencil.
What colour is it?
It's pink and grey.

2 What's this?
It's a chair.
What colour is it?
It's brown and green.

My classroom

1 **Read and match.**

1

Shopping list
pencil
rubber
ruler
pen

2

Shopping list
pencil case
rubber
ruler
notebook

3

Shopping list
pen
rubber
ruler
notebook

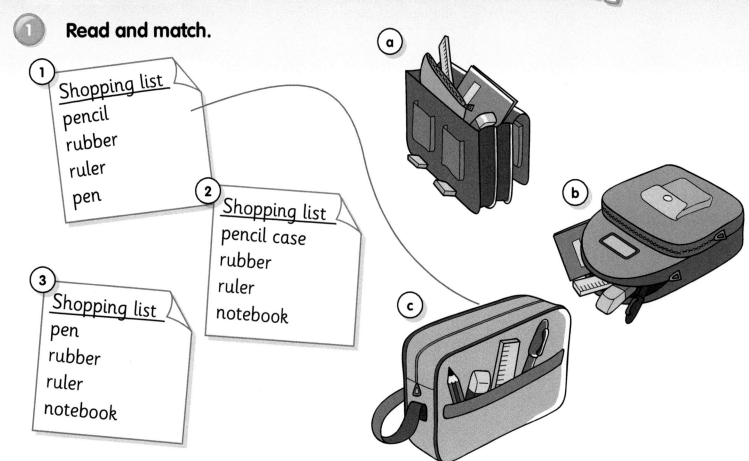

a

b

c

2 **Read and colour.**

This is my bag. It's green and orange.

This is my pencil case. It's yellow and purple.

This is my pen. It's black.

This is my ruler. It's brown.

This is my rubber. It's red and white.

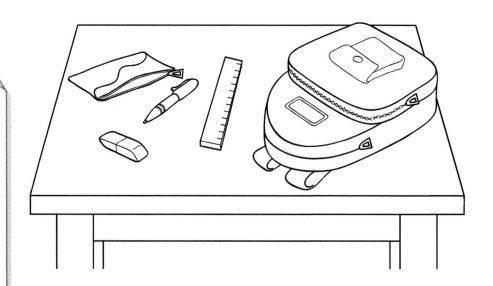

3 **Circle the sentences. Then count.**

1 (This is my bag.)   1

2 This is my pencil case. It's red and blue.   _____

3 This is my classroom. Here's the board. It's white.   _____

4 This is my desk. This is my chair. This is my notebook. It's red.   _____

What about you?

4 **What's in your school bag? Circle.**

pencil case   pen   pencil   notebook   rubber   ruler

5 **Draw and colour three things in your bag. Then write.**

This is my bag.

This is my _____ . It's _____ .

This is my _____ . It's _____ .

This is my _____ . It's _____ .

1 Match and colour.

1

black cars

blue dolls

red balloons

2

yellow stickers

purple crayons

3

pink bags

4

5

6

2 Count and circle.

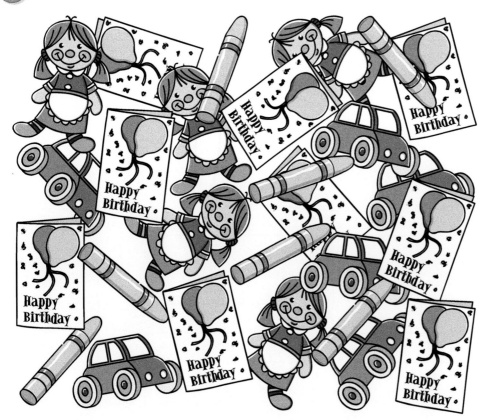

1 three / (five) dolls

2 seven / six cars

3 nine / four cards

4 seven / ten crayons

12

3 **Choose and write.**

dolls   balloons   ~~cars~~   stickers   crayons   rubbers

1 What are they?
They're ___cars___ .

2 What are they?
They're _____ .

3 What are they?
They're _____ .

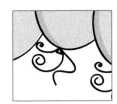

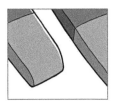

4 What are they?
They're _____ .

5 What are they?
They're _____ .

6 What are they?
They're _____ .

4 **Choose and write. Use** It's a **,** It's an **or** They're **.**

octopus   cards   ~~ball~~   doll   chairs   elephant

1 What's this?
___It's a ball.___

2 What are they?
_____

3 What's this?
_____

4 What are they?
_____

5 What's this?
_____

6 What's this?
_____

2b That's a robot!

1 **Find, choose and write.**

~~robot~~   doll   cake   watch

1 It's a ___robot___ !
Thank you!

2 It's a _____ !
Thank you!

3 It's a _____ !
Thank you!

4 It's a _____ !
Thank you!

2 **Look, read and match.**

1 What's this?

2 What are they?

3 What are they?

4 What's that?

a They're my presents.

b It's my birthday cake.

c That's a robot.

d They're my cards.

Happy Birthday!

Listen and colour.

1  **2**  **3**

4 **Look and write. Use** This is **or** That's.

1 ___This is___ a book.
___That's___ a bag.

2 _____ a cake.
_____ a robot.

3 _____ a whale.
_____ a penguin.

4 _____ a car.
_____ a doll.

2c The frogs!

1 **Read, look and match.**

a Open the window!   **b** Sit down, please!   **c** ~~Close the door!~~   **d** Stand up!

2 **Find, circle and match.**

1

2

3

4
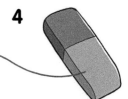

5

6

a	r	u	b	b	e	r
w	i	n	d	o	w	b
f	e	b	o	a	c	o
h	n	o	o	r	c	o
e	r	w	r	d	b	k
t	e	a	c	h	e	r

3 Circle groups of ten and write.

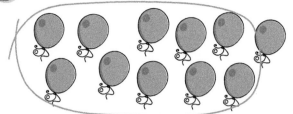

1 ten + one = _eleven_ balloons

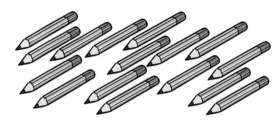

2 ten + six = _____ pencils

3 ten + _____ = _____ crayons

4 ten + three = _____ robots

5 ten + _____ = _____ presents

6 ten + _____ = _____ dolls

What about you?

4 What's in your classroom? Circle and write how many.

one board
_____
_____
_____
_____
_____

Social science

1 **Look and circle.**

  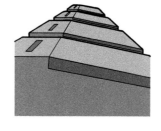 

1 (canteen) / hall   **2** canteen / office   **3** hall / classroom   **4** library / canteen

2 **Match and write.**

a

b

| c | **1** That's Mr Smith. He's the secretary. He's in the ___office___ . |

2 That's Miss Brown. She's the cook. She's in the _____ .

c

3 That's Mr Jones. He's my teacher. He's in the _____ .

d

4 That's Sam. He's a pupil. He's in the _____ .

e

5 That's Mrs Bell. She's the head teacher. She's in the _____ .

Review 1

1 **Look and write** What's this? **or** What are they? **Then tick or cross.**

1   ___What's this?___   It's a car.   ✔

2   _____   They're balloons.   ☐

3   _____   They're desks.   ☐

4   _____   It's a board.   ☐

5   _____   They're presents.   ☐

6   _____   It's a doll.   ☐

My English

2 **Circle and check.**

1 This is / That's a card and that's a ruler.   ☐

2 It's a / an elephant.   ☐

3 It's / They're my stickers.   ☐

Now colour.   ✔ = 😐 OK   ✔✔ = 🙂 Good   ✔✔✔ = 😃 Excellent

3a — She's pretty.

1 Find and circle. Then match and write.

wwbrothermtdadixsisterbqfamilyglmum

1 _____

2 _____

3 __brother__

4 _____

5 _____

2 Colour the 👨 words blue and the 👩 words red.

mum   brother
sister   dad

3 **Look and circle.**

1 (She's) / He's my sister.

2 She's / He's my mum.

3 She's / He's my dad.

4 She's / He's my brother.

4 **Look and write. Use** I'm**,** He's **or** She's**.**

2 Hello! _____ Karla. _____
a kangaroo. This is Chatter.
_____ a monkey.

1 Hi! _I'm_ Sally.
This is Tag. _____ a tiger.

3 Hello! _____ Tag. _____ a tiger.
This is Karla. _____ a kangaroo.

Is he your grandpa?

1 Listen and number. •))

2 Look, choose and write.

grandma   brother   grandpa   ~~mum~~

1  She's my _____mum_____.

2 He's my _____.

3  He's my _____.

4 She's my _____.

3 **Look and circle.**

1 Is he a boy?
(Yes, he is.)/
No, he isn't.

2 Is she a girl?
Yes, she is. /
No, she isn't.

3 Is she a teacher?
Yes, she is. /
No, she isn't.

4 Is he a baby?
Yes, he is. /
No, he isn't.

4 **Read and match.**

1 Is your name Patty?
2 Are you a girl?
3 Is Sally your friend?
4 Is Trumpet your brother?
5 Are you a teacher?
6 Is your grandma a teacher?

a Yes, I am.
b No, I'm not.
c No, he isn't.
d No, she isn't.
e Yes, it is.
f Yes, she is.

5 **Answer about you. Write** Are **or** Is **and circle.**

1 __Is__ your name Tag?   Yes, it is. /(No, it isn't.)
2 _____ you a boy?   Yes, I am. / No, I'm not.
3 _____ you a girl?   Yes, I am. / No, I'm not.
4 _____ your dad a teacher?   Yes, he is. / No, he isn't.
5 _____ your mum pretty?   Yes, she is. / No, she isn't.

3c — My family

1 Read, find and write.

Box 1: _____
Box 2: ___Anna___
Box 3: _____
Box 4: _____

Hello. My name is Anna. I'm a girl. I'm eight.
This is my school. This is my class. Look! This is me.
This is Emma. She's a pupil in my class.
She's my friend. She's seven. She's pretty.
That's Tom. He's a boy. He's my friend, too.
He's eight. He's funny.
That's my teacher. He's Mr Jones. He's nice.

2 Read again and answer. Use Yes, he/she is or No, he/she isn't.

1 Is Anna eight? _____Yes, she is._____

2 Is Emma a boy? _____

3 Is Tom twelve? _____

4 Is Tom funny? _____

5 Is Mr Jones a secretary? _____

6 Is Mr Jones nice? _____

3 Look. Then circle capital letters and full stops.

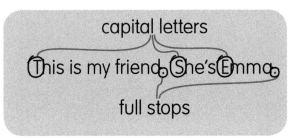

1 My name is Anna.
2 I'm a girl.
3 I'm eight.

4 Write with capital letters and full stops.

1 this is my friend   This _____
2 he's stefan   _____
3 he's eleven   _____

What about you?

5 Draw and write about you.

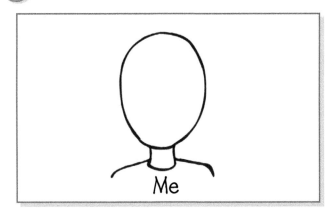

My name is _____.
I'm a _____.
I'm _____.

6 Choose one. Then draw and write.

friend   brother   sister   teacher

This is _____.
He's / She's _____.
_____
_____

25

We're cowboys.

 Read and match.

1

2

3

She's a dancer.

He's a spy.

He's a cowboy.

It's a box.

She's a teacher.

He's a boy.

4

5

6

2 **Look and answer. Use** Yes, he/she/it is **or** No, he/she/it isn't.

1 Is he a baby?

No, he isn't.

2 Is she a spy?

_____

3 Is it a box?

_____

4 Is she a teacher?

_____

5 Is he a spy?

_____

6 Is he a cowboy?

_____

3 **Look and circle.**

1 (They're) / We're **boys.**

2 We're / You're **girls.**

3 We're / They're **friends.**

4 (They're) / You're **clothes.**

4 **Look, choose and write.**

We're dancers. ~~We're teachers.~~ You're sisters. You're cowboys.

1 _We're teachers._

2 _____

3 _____

4 _____

Are we pirates?

1 **Listen and number.** 🔊

2 **What can you see in 1? Tick. Then count and write how many.**

1 ☐ _____ cowboys

2 ✔ __one__ spy

3 ☐ _____ queens

4 ☐ _____ dancers

5 ☐ _____ box

6 ☐ _____ king

7 ☐ _____ clown

8 ☐ _____ pirates

9 ☐ _____ kangaroo

10 ☐ _____ teacher

3 **Look and write.**

1 They're ___cowboys___ .

2 We're _____ .

3 They're _____ .

4 **Look and circle.**

1 Are you pirates?

(Yes, we are.) / No, we aren't.

2 Are we cowboys?

Yes, we are. / No, we aren't.

3 Are they clowns?

Yes, they are. / No, they aren't.

4 Are you dancers?

Yes, we are. / No, we aren't.

5 **Read, choose and write.**

we   they   No   aren't   ~~you~~   are

①

Are __you__ teachers?

Yes, _____ are.

No, we _____.
We're kings.
Are you clowns?

②

Are _____ dancers?

_____, we aren't.
We're robots.

Yes, they _____.
Are you pirates?

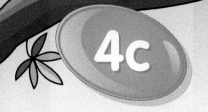

4c The grey duck

1 **Read, look and match.**

a No, I'm not. **b** Yes, you are! **c** We're swans.
d ~~Hello, Mum.~~ **e** No, she isn't.

1 Hello. I'm your mum.

d

2 Hello. Are you my mum?

_____

3 Is she my sister?

_____

4 Am I a swan?

_____

2 **Look and match.**

1    It's a duck.   2
    It's a swan.

3   He's happy.   4
     He's sad.

5   It's big.   6
     It's small.

3 Look. Then choose and write.

> I**'m** = I **am** He**'s** = He **is** We**'re** = We **are**
>
> You**'re** = You **are** She**'s** = She **is** They**'re** = They **are**
>
> It**'s** = It **is**
>
> **Look!**
>
> She**'s** Mary. BUT Her name **is** Mary.

_____I'm_____ Mary. This ____is____ a picture of my family.

My family _____ small.

This _____ my brother, Tom. _____ eleven.

This _____ my mum. _____ pretty.

This _____ my dad. _____ nice.

My grandma and grandpa _____ in the picture, too.

We _____ happy.

What about you?

4 Draw or stick a photo. Then write about your family.

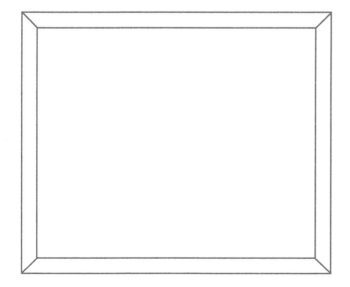

I'm _____ .

This is a picture of my family.

This _____

_____ .

This _____

_____ .

This _____

_____ .

1 Choose and write. Then match.

thirty   eighty   ~~twenty~~   seventy   sixty   forty   ninety

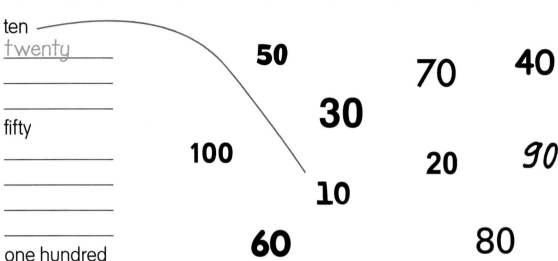

ten
twenty
_____
_____
fifty
_____
_____
_____
_____
one hundred

50   70   40
30   100
20   90
10
60   80

2 Look and circle.

1

70 + 3

thirty-seven /
(seventy-three)

2

20 + 6

sixty-two /
twenty-six

3

50 + 7

fifty-seven /
seventy-five

4

30 + 5

thirty-five /
fifty-three

3 Write.

1 Thirty and six is   thirty-six   .   30 + 6 = 36
2 Sixty and seven is _____.   ___ + ___ = ___
3 Forty and eight is _____.   ___ + ___ = ___
4 Twenty and two is _____.   ___ + ___ = ___
5 Eighty and one is _____.   ___ + ___ = ___
6 Fifty and four is _____.   ___ + ___ = ___

Review 2

1 **Look, read and write.**

Look! It's my (1) YRIBADHT _birthday_ .

I'm a cowboy. This is my (2) YMALIF _____ . My grandma is a

(3) CRENDA _____ . My (4) PRAGNDA _____ is a king.

My mum is a queen and my dad is a (5) YPS _____ . My brother is a

(6) LOCNW _____ and my (7) ITRESS _____ is a pirate.

My friend is a (8) DKCU _____ .

My English

2 **Circle and check.**

1 He's a king / pirate. ☐

2 Are they spies?
   Yes, they are. / No, they aren't. ☐

3 They're / We're friends. ☐

Now colour. ✔ = 😐 OK   ✔✔ = 🙂 Good   ✔✔✔ = 😀 Excellent

5a

It's his kite.

1 Find and circle. Then match and write.

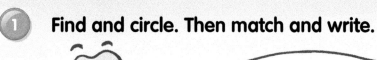

cl(kite)oradioubikedcomputergamey

1 It's a ___kite___ . **2** It's a _____ . **3** It's a _____ . **4** It's a _____ .

2 Look at 1 and complete.

It's _c_ _l_ _ _ _ _ _ .

3 Read, look and write. Use *my*, *your*, *old* or *new*.

1 Is this ___your___ radio?

2 No. ___My___ radio isn't old. It's ___new___ .

2 Is that _____ bike?

No. That bike is _____ . _____ bike is _____ .

3 Look, this is _____ computer game. It's _____ . It isn't _____ .

4 **Write** His **or** Her **and colour.**

1 __His__ kite is red.
2 _____ radio is black.
3 _____ computer game is green.
4 _____ bike is blue.

5 _____ robot is grey.
6 _____ ball is orange.
7 _____ books are pink.

5 **Match and write. Use** my, your, his, her **or** its.

He's __my__ dad. His car is big.

2 I'm Tessa and I'm eight. She's _____ sister.
_____ name is Sue.

3 Is that _____ brother?
Yes. _____ name is Tom. He's small.

4 This is _____ rabbit.
_____ name is Floppy. It's big.

5b They're our toys.

1 Circle and write.

clothes / (toys)   bikes / rollerblades   train / car

1 They're __toys__ .

2 They're _____ .

3 It's a _____ .

2 Look and write. Use slow or fast.

1 Penguins are __slow__ .

2 Tigers are _____ .

3 Hippos are _____ .

4 Dogs are _____ .

3 Circle the odd one out. Then write.

1 rollerblades	computer game	kite	(grandma)	_grandma_
2 swan	radio	kite	doll	_____
3 slow	prize	fast	old	_____
4 bike	train	winner	car	_____

4 **Listen and match.**

1  **2**  **3**  **4**  **5**  **6**

5 **Look and circle.**

1 We're sisters. They're (our) / their toys. **2** Is that your / their mum?

3 Look at your / their kite. **4** This is your / our cat.

6 **Read and write. Use** our, her, their, your **or** his.

1 We're sisters. _____Our_____ names are Maria and Anna.

2 They're our brothers. _____ names are Tom and Bill.

3 He's our dad. _____ car is old.

4 She's our mum. _____ car is fast.

5 You're our friends. _____ rollerblades are cool.

5c Our favourite toys

1 **Read, match and colour.**

1 Here are my toys. This is my radio. It's blue. They're my rollerblades. They're green. This is my ball. It's grey. This is my favourite toy. It's my computer game. It's yellow.

2 Here are my toys. This is my robot. It's red. This is my doll. It's purple. It's my favourite toy. This is my yo-yo. It's orange. This is my kite. It's pink and black.

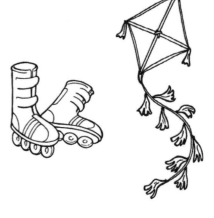

2 **Read again and write** yes **or** no.

1 His radio is blue. __yes__

2 Her favourite toy is her yo-yo. _____

3 Her kite is orange. _____

4 His rollerblades are yellow. _____

5 His computer game is his favourite toy. _____

6 Her robot is red. _____

38

3 **Find and circle. Then write with capital letters and full stops.**

1 (here)(are)mybirthdaypresents
   Here are my birthday presents.

2 myfavouritetoyismydoll

_____

3 thisismytrain

_____

4 myrollerbladesareorange

_____

5 mycarisblueandgrey

_____

What about you?

4 **Circle your toys.**

train   doll   car   computer game   kite   ball   bike   radio

5 **Draw and write about your toys.**

Here are my toys.
This is my _____.
It's _____.
This is my _____.
It's _____.
My favourite toy is my _____
_____.
It's _____.

1 **Choose and write.**

body   arm   feet   hand   ~~head~~   leg

1 _head_

2 _____

3 _____

4 _____

5 _____

6 _____

2 **Look and write a or b.**

ⓐ

ⓑ

1 I've got eight legs and feet.   _b_

2 I've got six legs and feet.   _____

3 I've got a black and yellow body.   _____

4 I've got a long, red body.   _____

5 I haven't got wings.   _____

6 I've got four wings.   _____

7 I've got a black head.   _____

8 I haven't got a black head.
   I've got a red head.   _____

3 Read and match.

1
She's got a cat.   2

They've got a dog.

He's got a rabbit.   4

We've got a goat.

4 Write He's/She's got or We've/They've got. Then draw.

1 ___She's got___ a yo-yo.

2 _____ a present.

3 _____ a kite.

4 _____ a bike.

5 Write about you. Use I've got or I haven't got.

1 _____ a bag.

2 _____ a ball.

3 _____ a computer game.

4 _____ a watch.

5 _____ a pet.

6 _____ a bike.

1 **Do the crossword.**

eyes   mouth   ~~nose~~   ears   head   hair

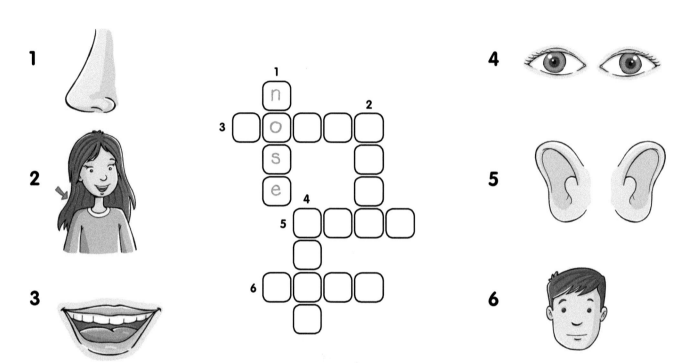

1

2

3

4

5

6

1

2
3 n
o
s
e
4
5
6

2 **Read, match and colour.**

1 He's got big ears. He's got a big nose.
He's got a small mouth. He's got blue eyes.

2 He's got small ears. He's got a small nose.
He's got a big mouth. He's got brown eyes.

3 She's got black hair. She's got small ears.
She's got a big mouth. She's got brown eyes.

4 She's got a big nose. She's got big ears.
She's got a small mouth. She's got blue eyes.

a

b

c

d

3 **Listen and number.** •))

(a)  ☐

(b)  ☐

(c)  ☐

(d)  [1]

4 **Write** has got **or** hasn't got.

1 A butterfly __has got__ wings.

2 A penguin _____ hair.

3 An octopus _____ eight legs.

4 A monkey _____ hands and arms.

5 A snake _____ feet.

5 **Write** has, hasn't **or** haven't. **Then match.**

(a)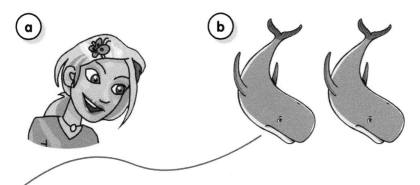

(b)

(c)

1 Have they got legs?
No, they __haven't__ .

2 Has he got a big nose?
No, he _____ .

3 Has she got a hair slide?
Yes, she _____ .

6 **Answer about you. Circle.**

1 Have you got red hair?   Yes, I have. / No, I haven't.

2 Have you got blue eyes?   Yes, I have. / No, I haven't.

3 Have you got big ears?   Yes, I have. / No, I haven't.

4 Have you got a small mouth?   Yes, I have. / No, I haven't.

1 Look, choose and write.

feet   long   ~~funny~~   strong   star   short   fast   trunks

Sam is at the circus.

The dancers have got beautiful (4) _____ and hands.

The monkeys are very (5) _____ .

The clowns are (1) __funny__ .

Their arms and legs are (2) _____ .

Sam has got (3) _____ arms and legs.

The elephants are (6) _____ . They've got big (7) _____ .

Sam isn't fast or strong. But look! He's a (8) _____ !

2 Circle the odd one out. Then write.

1 (long)	arms	hair	legs	__long__
2 feet	ears	big	trunk	_____
3 clown	funny	boy	story	_____
4 hands	eyes	beautiful	hair	_____

3 Look. Then circle the adjectives.

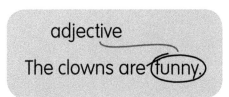

adjective
The clowns are funny.

1 The dancers have got beautiful legs.
2 The monkeys are fast.
3 The elephants are strong.
4 They've got big trunks.
5 Sam isn't fast or strong.

4 Look and write. Add the adjectives.

I've got eyes. (brown)
_____

I've got hair. (long)
_____

I've got a nose and a mouth. (small / big)
_____

I'm happy.

What about you?

5 Draw and write about a friend.

My name is _____ .
This is my friend, _____ .
He's / She's got _____ .
He's / She's got _____
and _____ .
He's / She's _____ .

Science

1 Read and match.

1 They've got four legs.
2 They've got black feathers.
3 They've got wings.
4 They've got scales.
5 They've got brown fur.
6 They haven't got legs.

a

b

c

2 Choose and write.

tails   scales   feathers   fur   ~~legs~~   wings

1 This is a snake.

Snakes have got

_____ .

They haven't got
_____legs_____ .

2 This is a zebra.

Zebras have got
black and white

_____ .

They've got long

_____ .

3 This is a swan.

Swans have got white

_____ .

They've got big, strong

_____ .

Review 3

1 **Look, choose and write.**

The girl has got a dog. Its ears are (1) _____long_____ and its (2) _____ are short. Her friend has got an old (3) _____ and a new bike. His bike is fast and her rollerblades are (4) _____ . He's got short (5) _____ and a big (6) _____ . She's got long hair and a small (7) _____ .

slow   ~~long~~   legs   kite   hair   mouth   nose

My English

2 **Circle and check.**

1 It's got six legs / heads. ☐

2 Her / Their radio is big. ☐

3 They have / haven't got a computer game. ☐

Now colour. ✔ = OK   ✔✔ = Good   ✔✔✔ =   Excellent

There's a town.

1 **Find and circle.**

1 It's a (playground) / park.
2 It's a house / town.
3 It's a river / swimming pool.
4 It's a swimming pool / tree.
5 They're children / clowns.

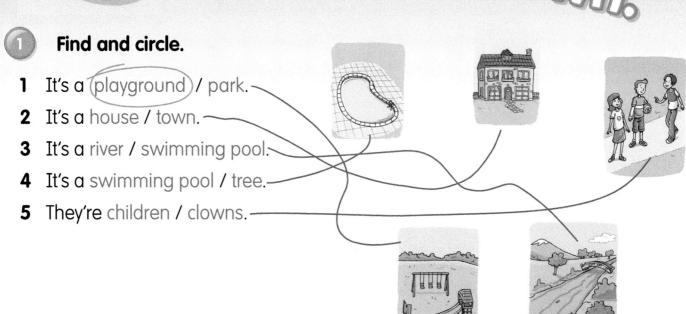

2 **Look, write and colour.**

1 I can see two pink __houses__ .
2 I can see four green _____ .
3 I can see three _____ .

4 I can see a blue _____ .
5 I can see eight red _____ .

3 **Look, read and circle.**

1	There's a river.	yes / (no)
2	There's a swimming pool.	yes / no
3	There's a rabbit.	yes / no
4	There are lots of trees.	yes / no
5	There are three children.	yes / no

4 **Look at 3 and circle.**

1 (There's) / There are a park.

2 There's / There are a nest.

3 There's / There are two children.

4 There's / There are lots of flowers.

5 There's / There are five trees.

5 **Look at 3 and write.**

	a big	dogs.
There's	two	girl.
There are	a white	ducks.
	a pretty	rabbit.
	three	boy.

1 _There's a big boy._

2 _____

3 _____

4 _____

5 _____

Where's Chatter?

1 **Look, choose and write.**

swings   treehouse   ~~climbing frame~~   nest   slide   children   river

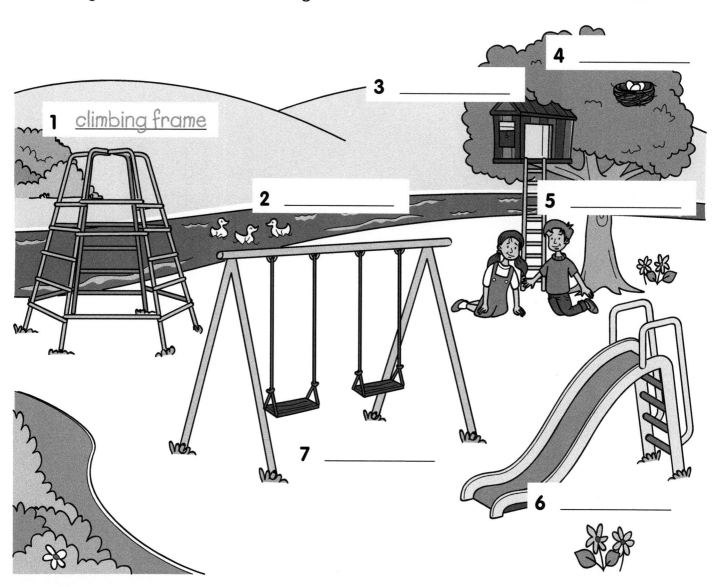

1 _climbing frame_

2 _____

3 _____

4 _____

5 _____

6 _____

7 _____

2 **Look at 1 and circle.**

1	There's a river.	yes / no	**5**	There's a slide.	yes / no
2	There are two children.	yes / no	**6**	There are two balls.	yes / no
3	There's a shop.	yes / no	**7**	There's a bus.	yes / no
4	There are two nests.	yes / no	**8**	There's a treehouse.	yes / no

3 **Listen and match.**))

4 **Look at 3. Choose and write.**

in   ~~on~~   under   next to

1 The cat is _____on_____ the chair.
2 The rabbits are _____ the flower.
3 The apples are _____ the bag.
4 The dog is _____ the umbrella.

5 **Look at 3. Choose and write. Use** Where's **or** Where are.

the book   the frogs   ~~the butterfly~~   the radio   the insects

1 _____Where's the butterfly?_____   It's on the flower.
2 _____   It's next to the dog.
3 _____   They're in the pool.
4 _____   It's under the chair.
5 _____   They're on the umbrella.

My town

1 Read and match.

a

b

My town is big. There are lots of cars and buses. There's a big park and there are lots of trees. There's a swimming pool but there isn't a river. There's a zoo but there isn't a circus.

 ①

 ②

My town is small but there are lots of shops and lots of cars. There's a school and a big playground. There's a swimming pool, too. There isn't a park but there are lots of trees.

2 Read again and match.

1 There are lots of cars.   1, 2

2 There's a big park.   _____

3 There are lots of trees.   _____

4 There's a big playground.   _____

5 There's a swimming pool.   _____

6 There's a zoo.   _____

3 **Look. Then circle** and **and** but.

> There's a school (and) a playground.
> There's a zoo (but) there isn't a circus.

1 There are lots of trees and flowers.
2 There isn't a river but there's a swimming pool.
3 There are lots of cars but there aren't lots of buses.

4 **Read and write** and **or** but.

> In my town there's a school __and__ a big playground.
> There are lots of shops _____ houses.
> There's a big park _____ there isn't a zoo.
> There isn't a swimming pool _____ there's a river.

What about you?

5 **What is there in your town? Circle.**

houses   trees   a swimming pool   a school   a zoo

a playground   a park   a circus   shops

6 **Stick a photo and write about your town.**

> My town is big / small.
> In my town, there's a _____
> and a _____.
> There are _____ and
> _____.
> There isn't a _____ but
> there's a _____.

1   Find, circle and match.

1

2

3

f	e	c	i	d	o	n
t	p	l	a	y	k	n
s	w	i	m	o	w	h
j	y	m	t	s	h	e
u	h	b	r	i	d	e
m	a	v	e	n	t	o
p	m	e	h	g	s	u

4

5

6

2   Read and match.

1 I can play   **a** a tree.
2 I can climb   **b** a bike very fast.
3 I can jump   **c** in the pool.
4 I can ride   **d** very high.
5 I can sing   **e** the guitar.
6 I can swim   **f** a song.

3   Look and write.

1 I can _climb a tree_ .   **2** I can _____.

3 I can _____.   **4** I can _____.

4 **Look and write. Use** He can**,** She can **or** They can**.**

1. __He can__ climb.
2. _____ sing.
3. _____ play the guitar.
4. _____ swim.
5. _____ ride a bike.

5 **Who is it? Find and write.**

	Paul	Tom	Eric	Me
🎵	✗	✗	✔	
🎸	✔	✔	✔	
🚴	✔	✗	✗	
🏊	✔	✗	✔	

1. He can sing and he can swim. He can play the guitar but he can't ride a bike.
   He's ___Eric___ .

2. He can't sing and he can't swim. He can play the guitar but he can't ride a bike.
   He's _____ .

3. He can swim and he can play the guitar. He can ride a bike but he can't sing.
   He's _____ .

6 **Complete the chart for you. Then write.**

I can _____ .

I can't _____ .

8b Can you skip?

1 **Do the crossword.**

~~swim~~   fly   run   skip   walk   carry   climb

1

2

3

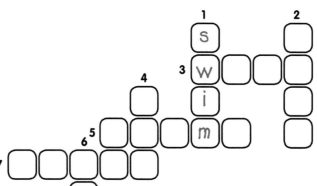
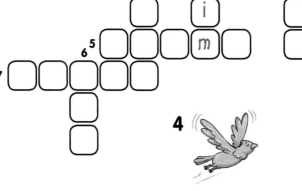

s
w i m

7

6

5

4

---

2 **Look, choose and write. Use** can **or** can't**.**

do a handstand   sing   rollerblade   ~~dance~~   ride a bike   swim

1 She __can dance__ .   **2** He _____ .   **3** She _____ .

4 He _____ .   **5** He _____ .   **6** She _____ .

3 **Listen and circle. Then write. Use** can **or** can't. •))

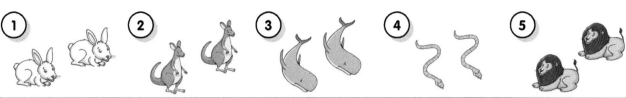

①	②	③	④	⑤
Yes, they can. / ~~No, they can't.~~	Yes, they can. / No, they can't.	Yes, they can. / No, they can't.	Yes, they can. / No, they can't.	Yes, they can. / No, they can't.

1 Rabbits/fly _____ Rabbits can't fly. _____

2 Kangaroos/run fast _____

3 Whales/walk _____

4 Snakes/swim _____

5 Lions/ride a bike _____

4 **Choose, write and answer.**

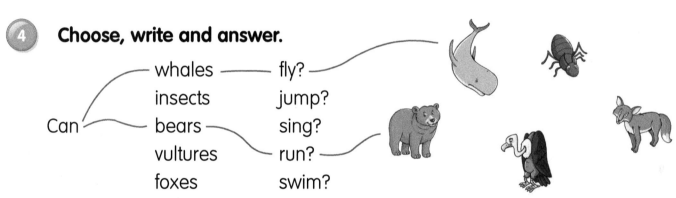

whales —— fly?
insects   jump?
Can   bears —— sing?
vultures   run?
foxes   swim?

1 _Can whales fly?_ _No, they can't._

2 _Can bears run?_ _Yes, they can._

3 _____ _____

4 _____ _____

5 _____ _____

5 **Write. Then answer about you. Use** can **or** can't.

1 _Can_ you do a handstand? _Yes, I can._

2 _____ you swim? _____

3 _____ you rollerblade? _____

4 _____ your mum ride a bike? _____

5 _____ your dad play the guitar? _____

6 _____ your friends run fast? _____

Where's my mobile phone?

1 **Look and write. Use** in, on **or** under.

1 Mum can't find her mobile phone.

2 It isn't ___on___ the desk.

3 It isn't _____ the cupboard.

4 It isn't _____ the computer.

5 It isn't _____ the table.

6 Fred's got the phone.
It's _____ his bed.

2 **Look. Then circle the commas. Underline** and**.**

comma

In the cupboard, there's
a rubber, a notebook
and four crayons.

1 In my school bag, I've got a pencil case, a ruler,
two pencils and a pen.

2 In my town, there's a park, a swimming pool, a
school and a zoo.

3 In the park, there are lots of trees, flowers, birds
and children.

4 In my bedroom, there's a bed, a cupboard,
a desk and a chair.

3 **Read, look and write.**

In my bedroom, there's a (1)  _____bed_____,
a cupboard, a bookcase, a (2)  _____
and a chair. There's a (3) 🖥 _____
on the desk. There are lots of books in the
(4) 📚 _____ .

What about you?

4 **What's in your bedroom? Circle.**

cupboard   desk   bookcase   radio   computer   chair
bed   guitar   clothes

5 **Draw and write about your bedroom.**

In my bedroom, there's _____
_____ .
There's _____ .
There are _____ .

Science

1 Match, choose and write.

hands   eyes   noses   ~~mouths~~   ears

1 We taste with our

2 We see with our

3 We hear with our

4 We smell with our

5 We touch with our

a _____ .

b _____ .

c ___mouths___ .

d _____ .

e _____ .

2 Choose and write.

~~I can taste~~   I can see   I can hear   I can smell   I can touch

1 ___I can taste___
my apple.

2 _____
the radio.

3 _____
a pretty butterfly.

4 _____
my dog.

5 _____
the flower.

Review 4

1 **Listen and match.** 🔊

2 **Look at 1 and write** yes **or** no.

1 There are two treehouses.   _yes_   4 There's a nest in the big tree. _____

2 There are four swings. _____   5 The boy can sing. _____

3 The girl can't skip. _____

My English

3 **Circle and check.**

1 Look! I can climb a tree / skip! ☐

2 Can goats fly?
Yes, they can. / No, they can't. ☐

3 There's / There are two nests in the tree. ☐

Now colour. ✔ = 😐 OK   ✔✔ = 🙂 Good   ✔✔✔ = 😃 Excellent

We like breakfast.

1 **Look and number.**

bread `3`   honey ☐   milk ☐   orange ☐

apple ☐   cheese ☐   water ☐   egg ☐

2 **What's for breakfast? Look and write.**

1 There's _____bread_____ and _____.

2 There are _____ and _____.

3 There's _____ and _____.

4 There are _____ and there's 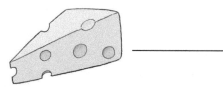 _____.

3 Look and circle.

1 I like / don't like oranges.

2 I like / don't like milk.

3 We like / don't like honey.

4 They like / don't like eggs.

4 Look and write. Use like or don't like.

| milk | ✓ | honey | ✗ | bread | ✓ | apples | ✓ | jelly | ✗ | oranges | ✓ |

1 Cats _____ like milk _____ .

2 Frogs _____ .

3 Ducks _____ .

4 Rabbits _____ .

5 Lions _____ .

6 Children _____ .

5 Write about you. Use like or don't like.

1 I _____ bread.

2 I _____ honey.

3 I _____ eggs.

4 I _____ oranges.

1 **Look and number.**

soup ☐ 1	fish ☐	potatoes ☐	sandwiches ☐
jelly ☐	cheese ☐	spaghetti ☐	chicken ☐

2 **What's missing in 1? Draw and write.**

1 _____

2 _____

3 _____

3 **Look and write.**

Do you like (1) 🍝
spaghetti for
lunch, Tag?

Do you like (3) 🥣
_____?

Yes, I do. But
I don't like (2) 🥣
_____.

No, I don't. But I like (4) 🍗 _____
and I like (5) 🐟 _____. I like
(6) 🥔 _____, too.

4 Listen and tick or cross. Then write. Use *likes* or *doesn't like.* •))

Jenny   **Tim**   **Anna**

✔

1 Jenny _____likes_____ apples.

She _____ potatoes.

2 Tim _____ chicken.

He _____ fish.

3 Anna _____ spaghetti.

She _____ soup.

5 Look, read and circle.

1 Do they like eggs?   (Yes, they do.) / No, they don't.

2 Do they like oranges?   Yes, they do. / No, they don't.

3 Do they like honey?   Yes, they do. / No, they don't.

4 Do they like fish?   Yes, they do. / No, they don't.

5 Do they like cake?   Yes, they do. / No, they don't.

6 Write. Then answer about you. Use *Yes, I do* or *No, I don't.*

1 __Do__ you like chicken?   _____

2 _____ you like spaghetti?   _____

3 _____ you like potatoes?   _____

4 _____ you like soup?   _____

5 _____ you like fish?   _____

What's on the menu?

1 **Read and tick.**

What do you want for lunch? I like sausages and chips. I don't like soup.

Peter

Luke

Dad

I like soup and chicken but I don't like eggs. I like oranges.

I don't like spaghetti or sandwiches. I like fish. I like cheese but I don't like jelly.

Menu

Soup ☐

Sandwiches ☐

Spaghetti ☐   Eggs ☐

Chicken ☐   Potatoes ☐

Fish ☐   Chips ☐

Sausages ☐

Oranges ☐   Jelly ☐

Apples ☐   Cheese ☐

2 **Read again. Who is it?**

1 He likes chicken. He doesn't like eggs. He's ___Peter___.

2 He likes soup and he likes oranges. He's _____.

3 He likes fish. He doesn't like sandwiches. He's _____.

4 He doesn't like jelly. He's _____.

5 He likes sausages. He doesn't like soup. He's _____.

6 He doesn't like spaghetti. He likes cheese. He's _____.

3 **What do they want for lunch? Read again and write.**

1 For lunch, Peter wants ___soup___, _____ and _____.

2 Luke wants _____ and _____.

3 Dad wants _____ and _____.

4 **Look. Then circle** and, or **and** but.

> I like pizza (and) salad.
> I don't like honey (or) apples.
> I like potatoes (but) I don't
> like oranges.

1 I like bread and honey.
2 I don't like tomatoes or potatoes.
3 We like chocolate but we don't like jelly.
4 They don't like sausages or spaghetti.
5 I like fish and eggs but I don't like water or milk.

5 **Write** and, or **or** but.

I like soup (1) __and__ bread. I don't
like chicken (2) _____ potatoes. I like
sausages (3) _____ tomatoes.
I like jelly (4) _____ I don't like biscuits
(5) _____ cake.

What about you?

6 **What do you like? Circle.**

soup   bread   spaghetti   fish   chicken   tomatoes
potatoes   apples   oranges   biscuits   jelly

7 **Draw and write about you.**

I like _____ and _____ .
I like _____ but I don't like
_____ .
I don't like _____ or _____ .

10a He gets up at seven o'clock.

1 **Number in order. Then choose and write.**

go to school   have breakfast   get up   ~~brush teeth~~

a ▢

b 1

c ▢

d ▢

brush teeth   _____   _____   _____

2 **Read and draw.**

1 It's one o'clock. **2** It's three o'clock. **3** It's five o'clock. **4** It's nine o'clock.

3 **Look and write.**

1 _It's two o'clock._   **2** _____   **3** _____

4 _____   **5** _____   **6** _____

4 **Look, choose and write.**

She has breakfast.　　She goes to school.　　She cleans her teeth.　　~~She gets up.~~

1

She gets up.

2

_____

3

_____

4

_____

5 **Choose and write.**

have / has　　go / goes　　~~get up / gets up~~　　clean / cleans　　play / plays　　like / likes

1 My name is Maria. I ___get up___ at seven o'clock.

My friend, Sue, ___gets up___ at eight o'clock.

2 I _____ to school at eight o'clock.

Sue _____ to school at nine o'clock.

3 I _____ lunch at one o'clock.

Sue _____ lunch at two o'clock.

4 I _____ fish and salad.

Sue _____ sandwiches.

5 I _____ the guitar every day.

Sue _____ computer games every day.

6 I _____ my teeth at eight o'clock.

Sue _____ her teeth at nine o'clock.

1 Find and circle. Then write.

WEDNESDAYSATURDAYMONDAYSUNDAYTUESDAYTHURSDAYFRIDAY

1 It's M __ nday.

2 It's T __ __ sday.

3 It's W _e_ dn _e_ _s_ day.

4 It's Th __ __ __ day.

5 It's F __ __ day.

6 It's S __ t __ __ day.

2 Look and write.

	Monday	Tuesday	Wednesday	Thursday	Friday	Saturday

1 Sam goes to the park on ___Saturday___.

2 He swims on _____.

3 He rides his bike on _____.

4 He goes to the zoo on _____.

5 He plays his guitar on _____.

6 He goes to school on _____.

3 **Listen and circle.** •))

4 **Look at 3. Write** Yes, she does **or** No, she doesn't.

1 Does Polly get up at nine o'clock every day? <u>Yes, she does.</u>

2 Does she eat bananas for breakfast? _____

3 Does she like apples? _____

4 Does she go to dancing school at eleven o'clock? _____

5 Does she go to bed at ten o'clock? _____

5 **Answer about you. Write** Yes, I do **or** No, I don't.

1 Do you get up at seven o'clock? _____

2 Do you go to school at nine o'clock? _____

3 Do you have lunch at one o'clock? _____

4 Do you go to the park after school? _____

5 Do you swim every day? _____

6 Do you play computer games every day? _____

10c Superboy!

1 **Read, look and match.**

a Help yourself, Superboy.   b Yes, I am.   c ~~It's my pleasure.~~

d Well done, Superboy!   e Have a good day, children.   f You're very good,

2 Look. Then circle the verbs.

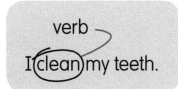

verb

I (clean) my teeth.

1 I go to school.
2 I play basketball.
3 I help my mum and dad.
4 I ride my bike.

3 Read, choose and write.

swim   go   play   ~~do~~   don't play   help   visit   ride

Every day after school I (1) ___do___ my homework and (2) _____ my mum and dad. I (3) _____ computer games. On Tuesday, I (4) _____ to the park and (5) _____ basketball with my friends. On Friday, I (6) _____ my bike. Every Saturday, I (7) _____ my grandma and grandpa. We (8) _____ at the swimming pool.

What about you?

4 What do you do after school? Circle.

do homework   play the guitar   play football
help my mum and dad   visit my friends   go to the shops
go to the park   swim   ride my bike

5 Write about you.

Every day after school, I _____.
I don't _____.
On _____.
On _____.
Every Saturday, _____.

1 **Look, read and match. Then write** healthy **or** not healthy.

a  ☐

b  1

c  ☐

d  ☐

e  ☐

f  ☐

1 Tina washes her hands after every meal. ___healthy___

2 Sandra watches TV after school. _____

3 Ben goes to bed at ten o'clock. He doesn't sleep well. _____

4 Julie eats sweets and biscuits. _____

5 Sam cleans his teeth every morning and every night. _____

6 Ted eats apples. _____

2 **Choose and write.**

well   watch TV   ~~healthy~~   sweets   night   fruit   morning

I'm (1) ___healthy___! I get up at seven o'clock in the (2) _____ and I go to bed at eight o'clock at night. I sleep (3) _____. I clean my teeth every morning and every (4) _____. I don't eat chips or (5) _____. I eat (6) _____. I don't (7) _____ after school. I play football with my friends.

Review 5

1 Look, choose and write.

doesn't   swim   ~~get up~~   sandwiches   goes   eggs   cleans   go

I'm Kate and this is my brother, Joe. I (1) __get up__ at 7 o'clock every day and I have (2) _____ for breakfast. Joe (3) _____ like eggs. He has (4) _____ for breakfast. He (5) _____ his teeth at 8 o'clock. I (6) _____ to school at 9 o'clock. On Sunday Joe (7) _____ to the park and I (8) _____ .

My English

2 Circle and check.

1 She gets up / cleans her teeth at seven o'clock.

2 He likes / doesn't like apples.

3 Does he play the guitar on Friday? Yes, he does. / No, he doesn't.

Now colour.   ✔ = 😐 OK   ✔✔ = 🙂 Good   ✔✔✔ = 😃 Excellent

I'm playing a game.

1 Find, circle and match.

h	q	c	d	r	i	d	e
i	f	a	p	l	a	y	u
d	l	r	h	k	d	v	c
e	y	r	i	z	x	y	l
c	q	y	r	e	a	d	i
l	s	l	e	e	p	s	m
e	a	x	i	p	c	i	b
a	g	c	o	m	e	k	k
n	v	r	a	t	e	r	g

1

2

10

9

8

3    4    5    6    7

2 Read and match.

1	do		**a**	a game
2	read		**b**	a bike
3	fly		**c**	my homework
4	play		**d**	a tree
5	climb		**e**	basketball
6	ride		**f**	a book
7	carry		**g**	my teeth
8	clean		**h**	my kite
9	play		**i**	a box

3 Look, choose and write.

coming   reading   ~~writing~~   playing   hiding   sleeping

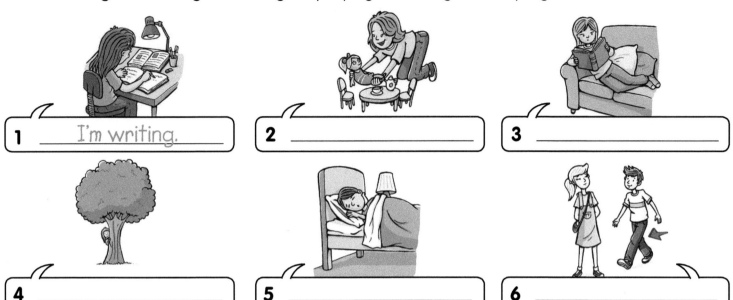

1 _____I'm writing.____

2 _____

3 _____

4 _____

5 _____

6 _____

4 Look, choose and write.

~~reading~~   writing   hiding   playing   sleeping   doing

1 She __'s reading a book__ .

2 He _____ .

3 He _____ .

4 She _____ .

5 He _____ .

6 She _____ .

They're having a shower.

1 **Look, choose and write.**

trousers   shorts   hat   shoes   ~~dress~~   T-shirt   socks   sweater   coat

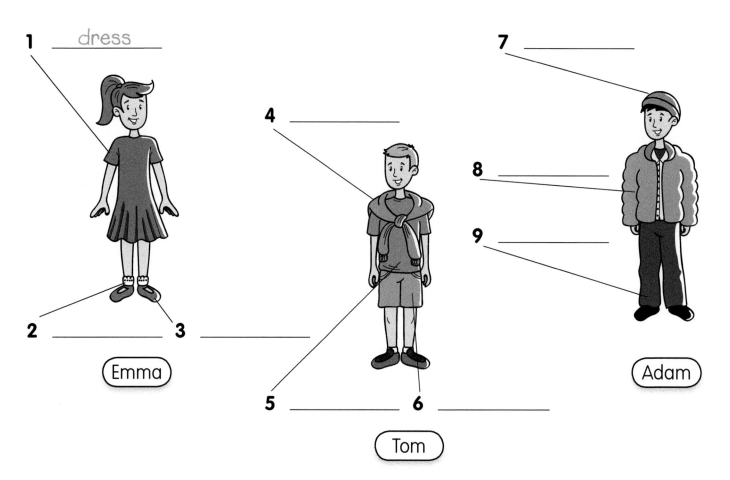

1 _dress_

2 _____ 3 _____

Emma

4 _____

5 _____ 6 _____

Tom

7 _____

8 _____

9 _____

Adam

2 **Look at 1 and write** yes **or** no.

1 Emma is wearing a dress.   _yes_   **6** He's wearing trousers.   _____

2 She's wearing a skirt.   _____   **7** Adam is wearing black shoes.   _____

3 She's wearing white socks.   _____   **8** He's wearing a coat.   _____

4 Tom is wearing a T-shirt.   _____   **9** He's wearing shorts.   _____

5 He's wearing a sweater.   _____   **10** He's wearing a hat.   _____

3 Listen and circle. •))

1

a   b

2

a   b

3

a   b

4
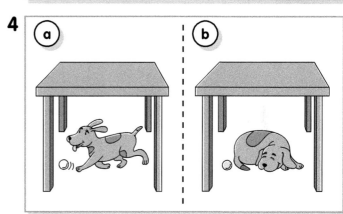
a   b

4 Circle, choose and write.

sleeping   hiding   ~~playing~~   reading

1 We're / (They're) ___playing___ .

2 We're / They're _____ .

3 We're / They're _____ .

4 We're / They're _____ .

Me and my friends

1 **Look, choose and write. Then match.**

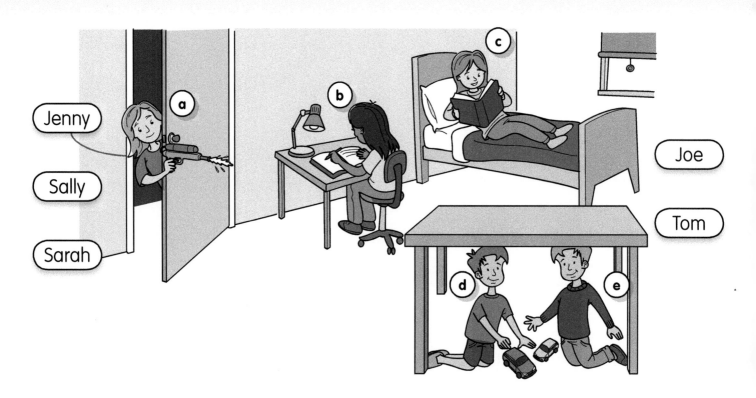

is doing   is wearing   ~~'m hiding~~   're playing   is wearing   is reading

My name is Jenny. Here's a picture of me and my friends. (1) I'm hiding _____ behind the door. My friend, (2) Sally, _____ a book. My friend, (3) Sarah, _____ her homework. My brothers, Joe and Tom, are under the table. (4) They _____ with toy cars. (5) Joe _____ shorts and a T-shirt. (6) Tom _____ trousers and a sweater.

2 **Read again and circle.**

1 Jenny is hiding behind the door. (yes) / no   4 Joe and Tom are playing.   yes / no
2 Sally is doing her homework.   yes / no   5 Tom is wearing a sweater.   yes / no
3 Joe and Tom are on the table.   yes / no   6 Jenny has got a water pistol.   yes / no

3 **Look. Then read and circle.**

He**'s** sleeping. ⟶ He **is** sleeping.
He**'s** got a kite. ⟶ He **has** got a kite.

Look at Tom.
1 He's wearing a sweater. (is)/ has
2 He's got a football.   is / has
3 He's reading a book.   is / has

Look at Jane.
4 She's got a radio.   is / has
5 She's got short hair.   is / has
6 She's pretty.   is / has

4 **Look and write.**

This is a picture of my friend, Sue.
(1) She _'s playing_____ with her doll.
(2) She _____ a skirt and a sweater.
(3) She _____ long hair.
(4) She _____ pretty!

What about you?

5 **Draw a picture of you and a friend. Then write.**

This is a picture of me and my friend,
_____ .
We're _____ .
My friend is wearing _____
_____ .
He's / She's got _____ .
I _____ .

1 **Do the crossword. Then write.**

volleyball   tennis   football   swimming

3

1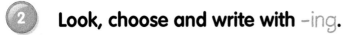

2

1

2

a

k

e

b

a

l

4

I'm playing _____.

2 **Look, choose and write with** -ing.

do   swim   ~~play~~   wear

1 He's ___playing___ the guitar.

2 I'm _____.

3 We're _____ our homework.

4 She's _____ a pretty dress.

3 **Look, choose and write. Use** 's **or** isn't.

riding / rollerblading   ~~doing / reading~~   walking / running   watching / playing

1  She ___isn't doing___ her homework.
She ___'s reading___ a book.

2  He _____.
He _____.

3  He _____ his bike.
He _____.

4 He _____ TV.
She _____ a computer game.

4 **Look and write.**

1 The rabbits ___aren't playing___ volleyball. They're _____.
2 The ducks _____ basketball. _____.
3 The frogs _____ football. _____.

1 **Look, choose and write.**

~~roaring~~   snoring   drinking   dreaming

1

The lion __is roaring__ .

2

The lion _____ .

3

The lion _____ .

4

The lion _____ .

2 **Look, choose and write with** -ing.

play / sleep   ~~eat~~ / drink   do / snore

She __isn't eating__ .
She _____ .

They _____
a game.
They _____ .

He _____
his homework.
He _____ .

3 Listen and circle.

1

ⓐ ⓑ

2

ⓐ ⓑ

3

ⓐ ⓑ

4

ⓐ ⓑ

4 Look at 3 and answer.

1 Is Sue watching TV? _____No, she isn't._____
What's she doing? _____She's doing her homework._____

2 Is Billy playing the guitar? _____
What's he doing? _____

3 Is mum listening to the radio? _____
What's she doing? _____

4 Are Jane and Molly swimming? _____
What are they doing? _____

5 Write. Use Is or Are. Then answer for you.

1 _____ you singing a song? _____

2 _____ your friends writing? _____

3 _____ your teacher playing the guitar? _____

85

1 **Look and answer.**

1 Is Jane in the bedroom?

No, she isn't.

2 Is she hiding under the table?

_____

3 Is Jane in the bathroom?

_____

4 Is she hiding in a cupboard?

_____

5 Is Jane in the kitchen?

_____

6 Is she hiding in the shower?

_____

7 Is Jane in the bathroom?

_____

8 Is she hiding in the bed?

_____

2 **Circle the odd one out. Then write.**

1	cupboard	table	bed	(garden)	_garden_
2	tennis	football	kitchen	volleyball	_____
3	shoes	dress	T-shirt	bathroom	_____
4	dream	giant	drink	eat	_____

3 **Look. Then read and circle the apostrophes.**

apostrophes
She isn't reading. She's sleeping.

This is my house. I'm in the living room. I'm playing with my friends. We aren't reading. My mum is in the kitchen. She's making lunch. My brother is in the bedroom. He isn't doing his homework. He's sleeping.

What about you?

4 **What are you, your family and your friends doing? Circle.**

playing the guitar   doing homework   reading   writing

sleeping   eating   drinking   having a shower   hiding   playing

5 **Draw and write about you, your family and friends.**

This is my house. I'm in the _____.
I'm _____.
My _____ is in the _____.
He / She _____.
My _____ is in the _____.
He / She _____.

Social Science

1 **Find and circle.**
Then write.

AMERICAINDIAJAPANSWEDEN

1 Junko lives in
J _____ .

2 Astrid lives in
S _____ .

3 Carl lives in
A_merica_____ .

4 Dev lives in
I _____ .

2 **Choose and write.**

flat   ~~mobile home~~   houseboat   wooden house

1
My name is Carl. I live in a
____mobile home____ in a park.
It's got two bedrooms, one bathroom,
a big living room and a small kitchen.

2
My name is Dev. I live on a
_____. It's got two
bedrooms, one bathroom, a small
kitchen and a small living room.

3
My name is Astrid. I live in a
_____. It's got three
bedrooms, two bathrooms, a big living
room and a big kitchen.

4
My name is Junko. I live in a
_____ in the city.
It's got one bedroom, one bathroom,
a small living room and a big kitchen.

3 **Read again and circle.**

	bedrooms	bathrooms	living room	kitchen
Carl	1 / ② / 3	1 / 2 / 3	small / big	small / big
Dev	1 / 2 / 3	1 / 2 / 3	small / big	small / big
Astrid	1 / 2 / 3	1 / 2 / 3	small / big	small / big
Junko	1 / 2 / 3	1 / 2 / 3	small / big	small / big

Review 6

1 **Listen and circle.** 🔊

1 What are the boys doing?

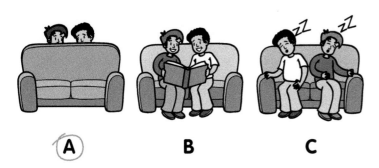

(A)   B   C

2 What's Gemma wearing?

A   B   C

3 What's John doing?

A   B   C

4 What's Nick wearing?

A   B   C

My English

2 **Circle and check.**

1 She's wet / dry.   ☐

2 We're / We aren't playing tennis.   ☐

3 Is she sleeping?   ☐
Yes, she is. / No, she isn't.

①

②

③

Now colour.   ✔ = OK   ✔✔ = Good   ✔✔✔ = Excellent

My Picture Dictionary

Listen, point and say. Then write.

_____

_____

_____

_____

_____

_____

_____

_____

_____

_____

_____

_____

_____

_____

_____

_____

_____

_____

_____

_____

_____

_____

_____

_____

_____

_____

_____

_____

_____

_____

_____

_____

_____

_____

_____

_____

_____

_____

_____

_____

_____

_____

_____

_____

4a

_____

_____

_____

_____

_____

4b

_____

_____

_____

_____

4c

_____

_____

_____

_____

_____

_____

5a

_____

_____

_____

_____

_____

_____

_____

_____ _____ _____

_____ _____ _____ _____

_____ _____ _____

_____ _____ _____ _____

_____ _____ _____

_____ _____ _____ _____

_____ _____ _____

_____ _____ _____ _____

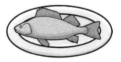

_____

_____

_____

_____

_____

_____

_____

_____

_____

_____

_____

_____

_____

_____

_____

_____

_____

_____

_____

_____

_____

_____

_____

_____

_____

_____

12a

_____ _____ _____ _____

_____ _____ _____

12b

_____ _____ _____ _____

_____ _____ _____

12c

_____ _____ _____ _____

_____ _____ _____

Cross-curricular links:

Parts of the school

_____ _____ _____ _____ _____

Classifying animals

Our senses

A healthy life

Other homes

Festivals:

World Animal Day

International Children's Day

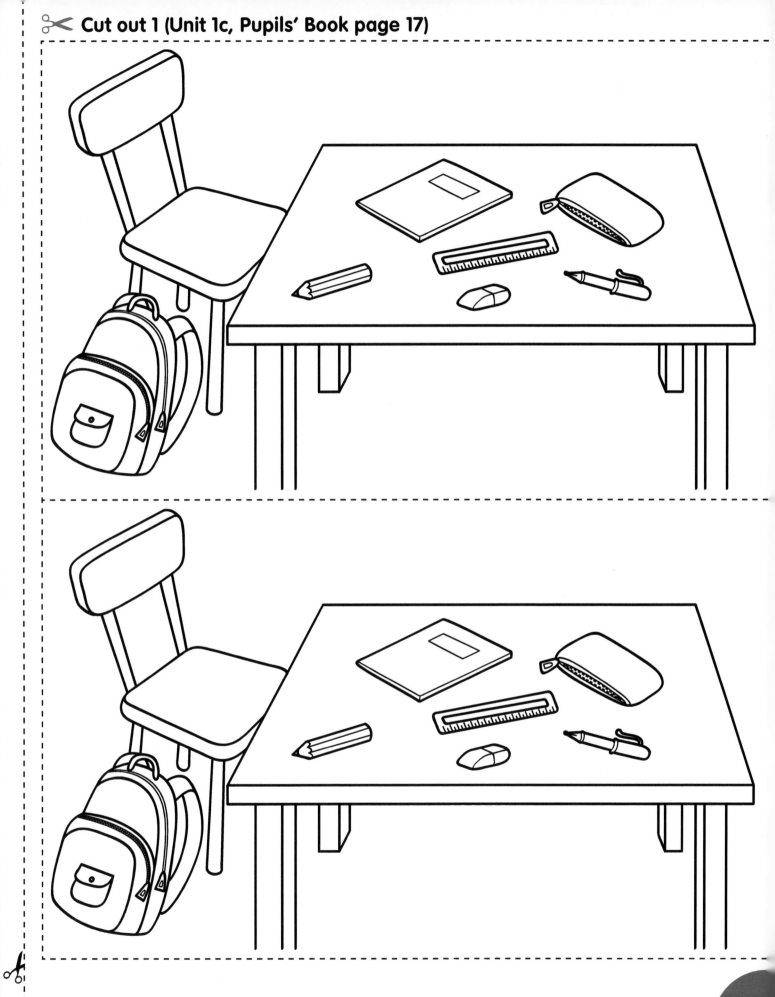

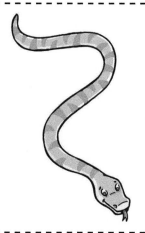

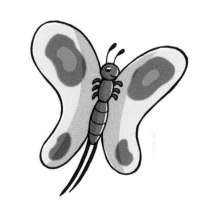

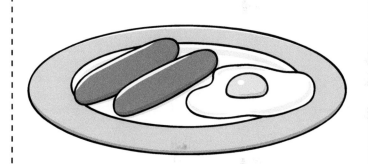

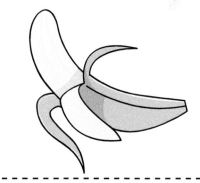